To Paul
Xmas
Love
Martin + Emma
x

The Pied Piper

A German Folk Tale

Retold by Cecelia Slater

Illustrated by Joel Iskowitz

MULBERRY EDITIONS

High in the mountains, next to a sparkling river, was the beautiful town of Hamelin. It was a happy place full of laughing children—until one day something terrible happened.

Rats—thousands of them—invaded the town of Hamelin. Suddenly big rats, small rats, brown rats, and white rats were EVERYWHERE. They scampered through the streets and into the houses, nibbling on cakes and pies, and hiding everywhere—even in the children's slippers.

The townspeople tried everything to get rid of the rats. They chased them with brooms, built huge traps, and even tried to scare them with loud noises. Nothing worked. Each day there seemed to be more and more rats.

The townspeople grew desperate. They demanded that the Mayor end the plague of rats.

The Mayor called a town meeting to discuss the problem. Many people gave speeches, but no one—certainly not the Mayor—knew how to get rid of the rats.

Suddenly a stranger entered the hall. The townspeople stopped their arguing and stared at the newcomer. No one had ever seen anyone like him.

He was twice as tall as the tallest person in Hamelin and his nose was long and pointy. His clothes were bright and colourful and a pink peacock feather topped his hat.

But most unusual of all was the sparkling silver flute hanging from his belt. It glittered like a rare jewel and glowed like the brightest star in the sky.

"Good afternoon," said the stranger with a smile. "I am the Pied Piper, and I can get rid of all the rats in Hamelin. But you must pay me 1,000 gold coins for my help."

"Why should we pay you so much," asked the Mayor, "when we cannot be sure that the rats won't return?"

"My fee may seem high," replied the Pied Piper, "but can you put a price on your town's happiness? As for trust, I give you my word the rats will never come back. All I ask is that you promise to pay me 1,000 gold coins."

The desperate townspeople forced the Mayor to accept the Piper's offer. They were sure that this magical stranger and his shining flute would somehow get rid of the rats.

The next morning the townspeople woke to the sweet sound of music floating through the air. The Pied Piper was playing his flute in the town square.

As the townspeople watched from their windows, thousands of rats began to pour into the square. They ran out of the houses, climbed down from the trees, and crawled up from the sewers. They came from every part of town.

Still playing his merry tune, the Pied Piper began to walk toward the river. The rats, as if under a spell, paraded after him.

When he reached the water's edge, the Pied Piper waved the rats onward. One by one, they jumped into the river and drowned.

Not a single rat was left in the town of Hamelin.

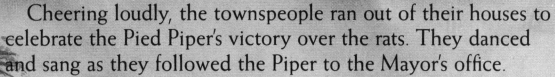

Cheering loudly, the townspeople ran out of their houses to celebrate the Pied Piper's victory over the rats. They danced and sang as they followed the Piper to the Mayor's office.

The Mayor was waiting for the Piper with a small bag of coins. "We thank you for your help," said the Mayor. "But the rats left so quickly and easily that you should be paid only fifty gold coins."

The greedy townspeople agreed with their sly Mayor. "The amount you ask is too much money for getting rid of a few rats," they said. "After all, 1,000 gold coins could feed everyone in Hamelin for a year."

The Pied Piper was furious. "I have kept my word, and now you must keep yours. I will give you one day to pay me what we agreed upon," he said. "I warn you, though, if you don't pay me, your children will."

The townspeople thought that was a fine joke. How could their children possibly pay the Piper?

The Pied Piper's deadline passed. The Mayor and the townspeople thought they had seen the last of him.

Suddenly, the first notes of an enchanting tune drifted through the town. The Pied Piper, tall and stern, stood in the square with his flute at his lips. As he played, sparks of anger seemed to fly from the gleaming flute.

Still, the townspeople laughed. "Perhaps he's hoping his music will weave a spell on our money and make it follow him out of town."

Soon, however, their laughter turned to tears.

As the Piper's music grew louder, children from all over Hamelin began to scamper into the square.

Soon every child of Hamelin was twirling and dancing happily around the Pied Piper.

With a wicked grin, the Piper began to walk toward the mountains. The townspeople, now terrified, began to call out to their children. Not a single child answered.

Like puppets on strings, the children followed the Piper up the steep mountainside and through a narrow passageway.

Suddenly, there was a loud roar. Rocks began to tumble and crash into the pathway. In a matter of minutes, the children were sealed behind a wall of rocks.

Only one lame boy, who could not keep up with the rest of the children, remained behind.

The townspeople searched high and low for a way through the wall.

The little lame boy looked for the passageway, too. He wanted to join his friends in the magical world the Piper's tune had described.

But the children were never ever found.

Today, a statue of the Pied Piper stands in the centre of Hamelin to remind everyone of the importance of keeping a promise.